D1373132

A PIGLET KIND OF DAY

Advance
PUBLISHERS

Advance Publishers, L.C.
1060 Maitland Center Commons, Suite 365
Maitland, FL 32751 USA

10 9 8 7 6 5 4 3 2 1
ISBN-10: 1-57973-397-2

Piglet was not having a very good morning. First he fell out of bed. Then he spilled haycorns all over the floor. Then he discovered all his clean pink sweaters had fallen off the clothesline into the dirt.

Pooh loves honey, but bears in the wild eat berries for a sweet treat.

BEARS

Bear cubs stay with their mommy. She keeps them safe. They follow her while they all look for sweet berries.

He went straight to Pooh's house and told his friend all about it.

As it turned out, Pooh was having a disappointing morning, too.

"One of my honeypots is empty," explained Pooh, "and that always gives me a very uneasy sort of feeling."

Trees hold all kinds of treasures—like honey and swings!

TREES

In the summer, many trees are covered with big green leaves, providing us with shade from the sun. Grass grows tall this time of year, and the sweet smells of roses, lilies, and other summer flowers often fill the air.

"I know what will cheer us up," Pooh said suddenly. He took Piglet by the hand and led him to the honeytree. Pooh scrambled up the trunk and was soon enjoying a sticky snack.

Poor Piglet would never be able to climb this tree!

GIANT SEQUOIAS

The biggest tree in the world is a giant sequoia. It's named General Sherman. This tree weighs more than 25 cars!

"Aren't you coming?" shouted Pooh. "There's plenty to share!"

"I'm trying!" replied a frustrated Piglet. But every time he managed to climb up the tree a few inches, he slid right back down again.

Finally, Piglet gave up. He sat down on a rock, feeling worse than ever.

Pooh, however, was in a much better mood. (Honey always had that effect on him.)

"Don't worry, Piglet," Pooh declared. "I have another idea!"

ROCKS

Rocks are part of the land. They are made of minerals, which are found under the ground. Minerals are made of different things such as crystals or metals. When groups of minerals get pressed together, they become rocks.

Kites aren't the only things that get carried by the wind.

WIND

Hold on to your hat! The wind is blowing. Sometimes the wind blows so strong that it makes a howling noise.

Pooh and Piglet searched until they found Christopher Robin. "Piglet needs some cheering up," Pooh explained.

"I know just the thing!" Christopher Robin answered, handing Piglet a bright red kite.

Wind can be very powerful!

WIND

We use some of the wind's energy to make machines and vehicles move. Windmills are farm machines that use the wind's energy to collect water or chop up grain, while sailboats use the wind's force to glide across the water.

Christopher Robin's kite soared into the air. "Yes!" the boy exclaimed. "Go, go, go!"

Piglet's kite also lifted off—taking Piglet right along with it! "No!" Piglet cried. "Whoa, whoa, whoa!"

The Hundred-Acre Wood is filled with happy creatures, incuding squirrels.

SQUIRRELS

The squirrels have fur. But their tails are not as bushy as they will be later on. Baby squirrels need their sleep. In a few weeks they will be playing and running all day.

"Piglet," said Pooh, "I am happy finding honey, and Christopher Robin is happy flying kites. But if we're going to cheer you up, I think we had better do the things that make you happy."

Seeds are small but sturdy, just like Piglet!

SEEDS

What is a seed? A seed is a little package that holds a baby plant. Most plants—from tall trees to little flowers—begin their life as seeds.

So Pooh brought Piglet to Rabbit's garden because he knew how much Piglet enjoyed planting. Putting a very small seed in a very small hole and covering it with a very small mound of dirt was the perfect activity for a very small animal.

Berry interesting!

STRAWBERRIES

These tasty strawberries are food for birds and animals like squirrels and bears. People can eat them, too. Yum, yum!

Then Pooh invited Piglet to go berry picking. Unlike the honeytree, the berry bush was close to the ground—just like Piglet! His basket was full in no time.

"Pooh, why is your basket only half-full?" asked Piglet.

"Because my basket and I are sharing," Pooh explained. He popped the sweet berry he was holding into his mouth, then put the next one into the basket.

FRUITS

Fruits can be soft and sweet like bananas, tart and crispy like apples, or even sour and juicy like lemons.

Birds make up special songs for each other, too.

BIRDS

Male birds sing loud songs in the spring so that female birds can find them. And a male bird's songs let other birds know where he and his mate are going to build their nest.

When the friends brought the berries home, Pooh had another surprise for Piglet.

"A song for you," he announced grandly. He played a happy tune with lots of high, sweet, Piglet-ish sort of notes.

SUN

Although it looks small in the sky, the sun is actually much bigger than the earth. In fact, the sun is about a million times bigger than the earth. If the earth were the size of a pinhead, the sun would be the size of a soccer ball!

Then Pooh drew something special for Piglet.

"It's wonderful, Pooh!" Piglet declared. "It looks just like me!"

In return, Piglet made Pooh a picture of a beautiful, sunny day.

Oak trees have lots of acorns, but even more leaves.

LEAVES

Leaves can look like hearts, ovals, fans, triangles, needles, and many other shapes. They can have pointed or rounded edges, and can be smooth, fuzzy, or even prickly to the touch.

Pooh was pleased to see a smile on his friend's face—and he was determined to keep it there.

"Come on!" he told Piglet. "There's a place I think you'd like very much."

Soon they arrived at the biggest oak tree in the Hundred-Acre Wood.

Piglet had never seen so many haycorns in one place before!

As he gathered them up, he thought of all the wonderful haycorn pies he'd be able to bake for his friends.

An acorn is a big seed from an oak tree, but some seeds are even bigger!

COCO-DE-MER PALM

The largest type of seed in the world is the coco-de-mer palm. It can weigh 50 pounds. That is as much as 30 coconuts!

The water in Pooh's stream is fresh and salt-free.

BODIES OF WATER

Oceans, lakes, ponds, rivers, and streams are all bodies of water. Oceans have salt water. Most rivers, lakes, and streams have freshwater.

When Piglet's sack was full, Pooh took him by the hand. "Follow me, " he said.

"Where are we going?" asked Piglet.

"To the stream!" Pooh replied.

"Are we going to play Pooh Sticks?" asked Piglet hopefully.

Pooh nodded. "Only today we're going to call them Piglet Sticks!"

RIVERS AND STREAMS

Salmon are one kind of fish that begin their life in a stream. When they grow up, they swim up the mighty currents of a river. They always return home to the exact place where they were born.

UNDERGROUND ANIMALS

Many animals make their homes in the soil. This mole spends most of its life underground. Moles dig long tunnels with their big, wide front claws. Moles find lots of yummy bugs and worms to eat in the ground.

After their game, Pooh suggested a Piglet parade. They didn't have any musical instruments, but that didn't stop this marching band!

"Rum-uh-tum-tum!" called Pooh.

"Rat-a-tat-tat!" cried Roo.

"Rooti-toot-toot!" sang Tigger.

"Clang," added Eeyore.

Because he was the guest of honor, Piglet was presented with a balloon and a honeypot.

"Oh my," said Piglet, "I don't think this day could get any better."

Thank goodness the clouds didn't rain on Piglet's parade!

CLOUDS

There are names for the different kinds of clouds. Soft, wispy clouds are called cirrus clouds. The big, puffy ones are cumulus clouds. Dark rain clouds are called nimbus clouds.

Piglet's blanket is casting a shadow.

SHADOWS

When the sun shines, it makes shadows. A shadow just shows the shape of something. It can be the shape of anything.

But it did. Piglet's friends placed him on a blanket and tossed him gently into the air.

"Hip-hip-hooray! Hip-hip hooray! It's a Piglet kind of day!" they chanted.

Usually Piglet was not very fond of high places, but with his friends surrounding him, he felt happy and safe.

"Wheee!" he cried. "Look at me!"

Piglet feels like he can touch the sky!

SKY

There is no end to the sky. You can see very far and very high. There are tools that help us see things even better. One of these tools is called a telescope. It makes things in the sky look brighter and closer.

MAMMALS

A mammal is an animal. Mammals can be big or small, striped or spotted. They can be brown, white, black, or even red. All mammals have hair or fur, and they all take good care of their babies. Mammal babies drink their mothers' milk.

At afternoon's end, Pooh walked a very happy Piglet back home again.

"Pooh," said Piglet, "the next time I'm feeling blue, please remind me how lucky I am to have a friend such as you!"